This Book Belongs to:

To our families, at home and at school, who have inspired and encouraged us to learn, grow, and try something new. And to our furry friends, who had a paw in bringing this book to life!

– Marie Weller & Paula Vertikoff

To my family.

– Marina Halak

Cranium Critters

Paws at the Pause Place

Text by Marie Weller & Paula Vertikoff
Illustrations by Marina Halak

A Note for GrownUps

The brain guides everything that we do: our body's movements, our decision making, and our emotions. Teaching children (and the adults who care for them) about the brain and how it functions, helps them understand the relationship between their thoughts, emotions, and behaviors. If knowledge is power, then learning about the brain empowers kids to control what they think, how they feel, and how they act. When feeling overwhelmed by a big emotion, they are able to identify what's happening in their brain and access calming strategies to regulate their emotions. The ability to manage emotions plays an important role in academic and life success.

How does the brain work?

Cranium Critters™ uses the metaphor of the safety pup and wise owl to help children understand the brain's fight, flight, or freeze response. The brain's amygdala acts like a safety pup, or guard dog, as it watches out for danger and regulates the brain's emotional state. When the dog is calm, we are able to think clearly because the prefrontal cortex (PFC), the wise owl part of the brain, is engaged and processing information effectively. But in the event of perceived danger or stress, the safety pup barks out an alert and takes over. As fear and anxiety increase, the brain's executive functions, located in the PFC, decrease, causing us to act – or react – without thinking. This is why we often speak or act irrationally when we are experiencing strong, intense emotions. In the animal metaphor, the safety pup's barking overpowers the wise owl or scares it away, leaving us to react to the perceived threat by fighting, running away, or freezing/hiding until the danger passes. When there's no real danger, an overactive response can create a problem or make an existing problem worse! Like real dogs, the amygdala sometimes treats situations that are unfamiliar as threatening or dangerous. Think of a pet barking when the Amazon driver delivers a package or a new friend visits, even though there is no threat of harm. Through reassurance and training, though, a child's inner dog can begin to know the difference and behave accordingly.

Why is this important?

There's a sense of power and relief that comes with the realization that we can control our brain, reduce our stress, and optimize our learning! But just like any other skill, emotion regulation is learned and developed over time. It needs to be *taught* and, more importantly, *practiced* when emotions are calm and regulated, and *supported* when emotions feel too big to handle.

Tools such as calming strategies, including mindful breathing and focused awareness exercises can help the brain's prefrontal cortex, or owl, function more effectively while learning and processing information. Incorporating emotion regulation practice into their daily routine, and allowing children to explore calming tools in a *Pause Place* (like the one on pages 30–31), will help them learn how to lower their stress levels and feel in control of their emotional responses when they need it the most.

The Cranium Critters™ engage children in learning how their brain works and establish brain-aware practices during the prime time for neural growth, setting them up for success in learning and life.

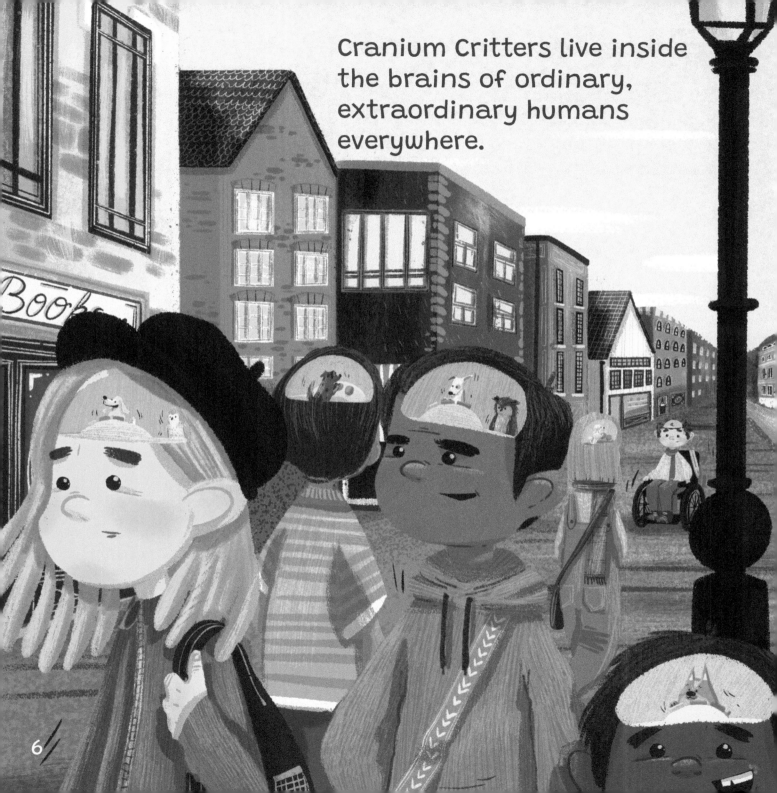

Cranium Critters live inside the brains of ordinary, extraordinary humans everywhere.

6

Meet Scout, the brain's safety pup. She is filled with energy, curiosity, and emotion.

Scout takes her safety responsibility seriously, so she is always on the lookout for **BIG** deals that might be...

harmful or dangerous.

If she sniffs out anything suspicious, she barks out one of her safety plans:

But like most pups, Scout is still learning. Sometimes she gets mixed up, and treats little deals like they are **BIG** deals

Little deals may be *different*, or *disappointing*, or difficult, but little deals are NOT *dangerous*. And when a Cranium Critter gets mixed up, it can cause trouble for their human!

Scout decides to take a brain break.

IS YOUR HUMAN ALWAYS IN TROUBLE?

ARE YOU AT THE END OF YOUR LEASH?

HAVE YOU BEEN BARKING UP THE WRONG TREE?

YOU'VE COME TO THE RIGHT PLACE!

Welcome to the Pause Place.
I'm Einstein, the brain's head thinker and problem solver. How can I help you?

Oh boy!
Am I glad to see you!
I need help with my human.

You mean **OUR** human. We are supposed to be working together.

You've been so busy barking and making a fuss over little deals, you haven't even noticed me.

BARK!

If we can find a way to calm that bark, we'll be able to work together. Then our human will be able to think clearly and solve problems.

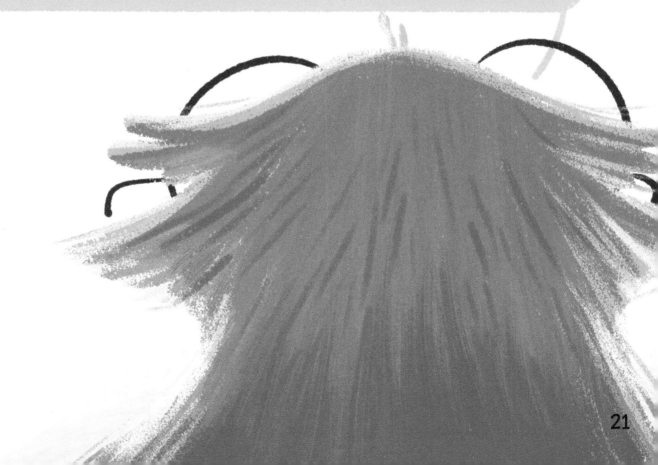

The Pause Place is filled with calming tools and helpful strategies that might work for us. Let's take a look around.

PAW PRINT BREATHING

BIG DEAL? LITTLE DEAL?

PROBLEM

DOWNWARD DOG

23

24

On the way home, Scout and Einstein feel cool, calm, and connected until they hear arguing in the distance.

FOOD

BLAH BLAH

SLEEP ZONE

The Cranium Critters put their Pause Place strategies to the test. Scout remembers the difference between **BIG** deals and little deals.

She reminds their human to breathe so that he can stay calm and hear Einstein's brilliant ideas. Together they solve the problem. *EVERYONE* feels safe and proud.

And the fun continues for the rest of the day.

Create your own Pause Place!

Find a quiet corner in your home or classroom. Fill the space with calming tools. Here are some examples to get you started:

Stuffed Animal (Rock-a-Pup)

Lie down on the floor and place a stuffed animal or similar object on your belly. While breathing in and out, notice how your belly moves up and down. Use your breath to rock and relax your pup. Feel your own body relaxing too!

Pencil & Paper (Paw Print Breathing)

Use a pencil or your finger to trace the outline of your hand. Breathe in as you move up each finger and out as you move down each finger.

Flower (Flower Breathing)

Use either a real flower, a photo, or a scented sticker. Inhale to breathe in the scent of the flower. Then slowly exhale. Repeat 3x.

Yoga Mat
(Downward Dog)

Begin on your hands and knees. Curl your toes under, straighten your knees, and lift your tail up to the sky. Feel stress and worry leave your body as you stretch and breathe.

Mirror
(Positive Pup Talk)

Look at yourself in the mirror. Talk to yourself using encouraging words. Give yourself a compliment. Say some good things about today. Remind yourself that you have the power to handle disappointments. You can do hard things.

Visit the space regularly to practice breathing exercises and strategies for calming your body and mind so that your brain's safety pup and owl can work well together.

About Authors:

Marie Weller and Paula Vertikoff are an Elementary School Counselor and Principal duo dedicated to social emotional wellness for children and the adults who care about them. With a combined fifty years of experience in education, they have seen over and over again what research has confirmed – social emotional wellness plays an integral role in academic and life success.

They have created Cranium Kids Media to share video lessons, stories, and activities to help young people understand their minds, recognize and manage emotions, and develop social awareness skills for learning and living. Their little life lessons provide the big life skills needed to lead happier, healthier lives.

About Illustrator:

Marina Halak is a Ukrainian illustrator and painter based in Germany. She loves experimenting with traditional materials and digital art and uses various media, including gouache, coloured pencil, ink and watercolours.

Her illustrations celebrate the best and funniest childhood memories, magic and humour. She loves to dive into imaginary worlds existing in her head and meet unique characters there.

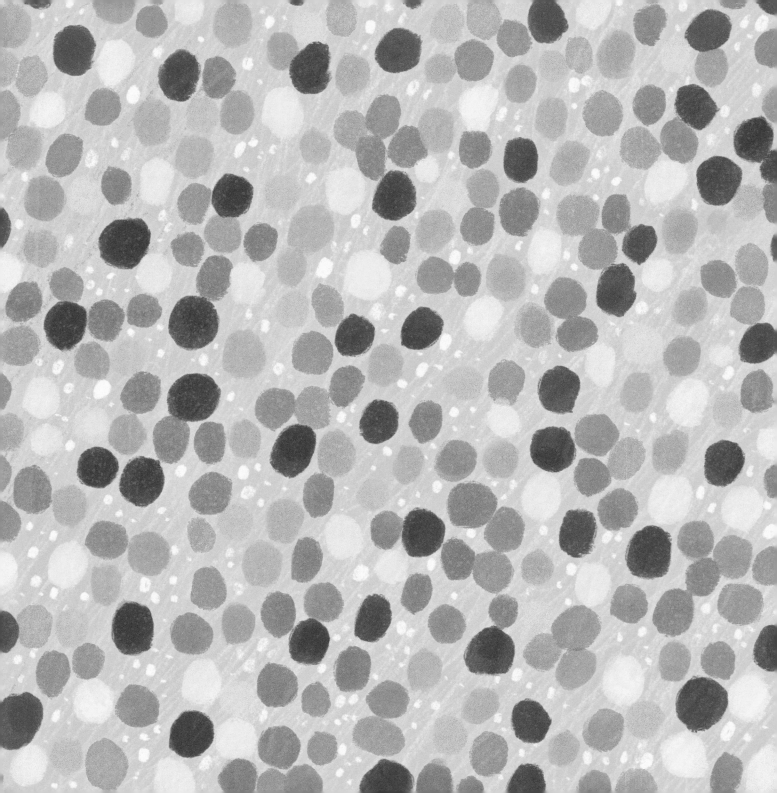

Lightning Source UK Ltd.
Milton Keynes UK
UKHW021017081222
413522UK00009B/83